FOLENS
IDEAS BANK
RE
HINDUISM

Christine Moorcroft

Contents

How to use this book 2

Introduction 3

Beliefs

Symbols 4

Hindu deities 6

Goddesses 8

Creation 10

People

Mahatma Gandhi 12

Brahmin 14

Brothers and sisters 16

Special Places

The mandir 18

A roadside shrine 20

The home shrine 22

Pilgrimage 24

Writings

The Ramayana 26

The Bhagavad Gita 28

Special Times

Samskars 30

New baby 32

Marriage 34

When someone dies 36

Festivals

Festival calendar 38

Janmashtami 40

Navaratri 42

Divali 44

Holi 46

Glossary 48

Folens Publishers

How to use this book

Ideas Bank books provide ready to use, practical, photocopiable activity pages for children, **plus** a wealth of ideas for extension and development.

Clear focus to the activity.

Suggestions for developing work on the photocopiable pages.

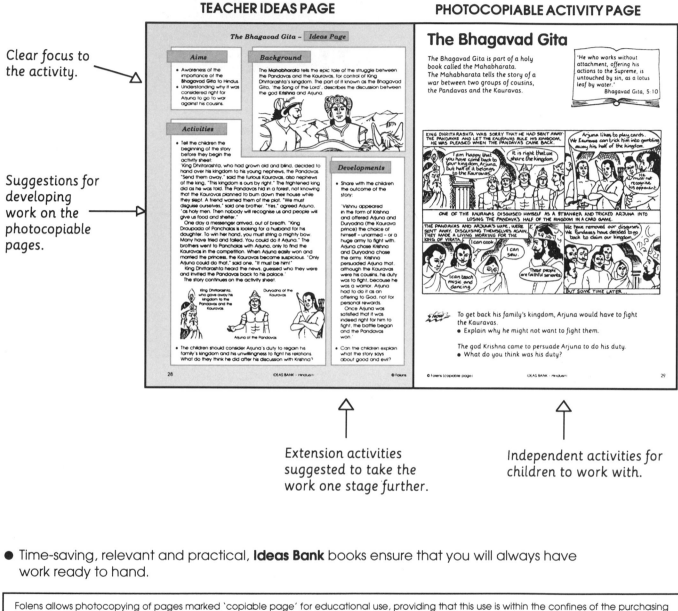

Extension activities suggested to take the work one stage further.

Independent activities for children to work with.

● Time-saving, relevant and practical, **Ideas Bank** books ensure that you will always have work ready to hand.

Christine Moorcroft hereby asserts her moral right to be identified as the author of this work in accordance with the Copyright, Designs and Patents Act, 1988.

Editor: Andy Brown
Illustrations: Tony Dover/Graham-Cameron Illustration
Layout artist: Patricia Hollingsworth
Cover by: Hutchison Picture Library
Cover design: In Touch Creative Services Ltd.

© 1995 Folens Limited, on behalf of the author.
Reprinted 1997

Every effort has been made to contact copyright holders of materials used in this book. If any have been overlooked, we will be pleased to make any necessary arrangements.
First published 1995 by Folens Limited, Dunstable and Dublin
Folens Limited, Albert House, Apex Business Centre, Boscombe Road, Dunstable LU5 4RL, England.
ISBN 1 85276 856–8
Printed in Singapore by Craft Print

Introduction

Ideas Bank: Hinduism presents Hinduism in an explicit way, acknowledging the needs of non-specialists for material that explains the main features of the faith while providing relevant and feasible classroom activities. It covers the needs of teachers and children from any religious background or none.

Structure

Beliefs, **People**, **Special Places**, **Writings**, **Special Times** and **Festivals** reflects the structure of most agreed syllabuses. This should be helpful to teachers in their planning. Different faiths attach differing degrees of significance to these aspects. The structure of this book reflects the focus in Hinduism on the place of faith in the home and the community and its relevance to the stages of a person's life. The section covering **Writings** focuses on the Ramayana and Bhagavad Gita because of their accessibility. Quotes from other writings such as the Vedas, Puranas and Mahabharata are a feature of the book, helping to make the link between children's activities and perceptions and explicit teaching about the faith itself. These writings are not covered in detail because of their inaccessibility to non-specialists.

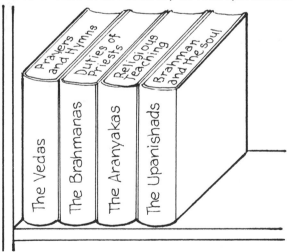

Hinduism

An important consideration while preparing this material has been ensuring that Hinduism is represented accurately and in a way that helps teachers to avoid inadvertently giving offence to members of the faith, as well as helping them to develop positive and respectful attitudes in the children. For example, it is made clear that while there are many Hindu deities, Hinduism is essentially monotheistic (a belief in one God). The rituals involved in worship are presented in a way that helps children to understand them rather than regard them as an elaborate pantomime.

Stereotyping has been avoided, noting that there are certain beliefs and practices common to all devout Hindus, but also variations in custom and practice.

Another consideration has been to present what may be unusual practices to some children in a way that develops understanding and empathy, rather than mere curiosity.

Activities

The book is designed to provide interesting classroom activities together with background information for the teacher as well as suggestions for extension activities.

Each activity is accompanied by sufficient information to enable the teacher to implement it without the need for further published material. It could be enriched by following the extension ideas on the teachers' page, which suggest how to make the most of visits, visitors and help from members of local faith communities, especially those already connected with the school. Support material is also suggested: music, works of art, poems and stories, along with ideas as to how to maximise their potential.

The activity pages are designed to be used in various ways, as noted on the ideas pages:
- to introduce a topic (drawing on the children's own experience)
- to continue exploration instigated by the teacher (finding out more about an aspect of Hinduism)
- to reinforce learning from activities described on the ideas page
- for recording findings or ideas.

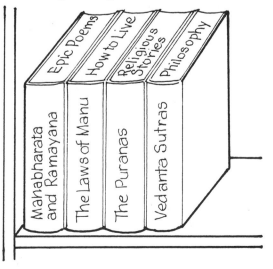

Aim

- To understand the concept of symbols in religion, in particular those important in Hinduism.

Activities

- The children could cut out, paste and label pictures of symbols used in everyday life. Can they explain how symbols are often more useful than words?
- Ask them to think of symbols that are special for particular groups of people:

Symbol	Group
trefoil	Girl Guides.
owl	supporters of Sheffield Wednesday football club.
kiwi	people of New Zealand.
stars and stripes	people of the U S A

- Saffron is the holy colour of Hinduism. Do the children know what colour saffron is? They could find out about the saffron crocus and its source. They could colour the symbols on the activity sheet saffron.

Background

The **swastika** is a sacred symbol believed by some Hindus to bring good fortune. It is often seen on Hindu wedding invitations and temple wall designs. Sometimes the swastika is carefully made on the temple floor with grains of rice, to be eaten by the birds that are allowed in.

The lotus looks just like a water lily. It is a symbol of purity because it grows in muddy water, yet remains pure white. Hindus believe that the human spirit should remain untouched by any surrounding corruption or impurity, like the lotus.

The **aum** is the most sacred of all Hindu symbols and is often used as a **mantra**, or special sound, that forms part of a prayer.

The mantra shown on the pupil page is written phonetically, enabling the children to pronounce it. It means:

'The protector, who is the foundation of the whole Universe, is self-existent and free from all pain and frees the soul from pain and troubles, exists throughout the Universe and sustains everything. He is the creator and energiser of the whole Universe, the giver of all happiness, worthy of acceptance, the most excellent purifier. Let us embrace that God so that he directs our minds.'

Developments

- Collect and display the sacred symbols of other religious groups:

Christianity

Islam

Sikhism

Buddhism

Judaism

- Provide reference books so that the children can research the origins of the symbols.

Symbols

The swastika, lotus flower and aum are holy symbols for Hindus.

'Aum Bhur bhuvah swah. Tatsavitur varenyam bhargo devasya, dhio yo nah prachodayat.'
An important Hindu mantra. Mantras often begin with 'aum'.

- Match the symbols to their names and meanings.

| swastika | lotus flower | aum |

A white flower that symbolises purity.

The sound that was made when the Universe was created.

A 'welcome' sign that is painted on doors.

- Think of something that is special to you.
- Draw a symbol for it.
- How might you use this symbol?

- Draw a picture story that shows what Hindus might think about when they see the swastika, lotus flower and aum.

Hindu deities – Ideas Page

Aim

- To develop an understanding of symbolism and the idea of Hindu deities as representing different aspects of one god, **Brahman**.

Background

Hinduism is essentially monotheistic. The various deities represent aspects of the one great deity, Brahman, not to be confused with **Brahma**, shown on the activity sheet, and **Brahmin** (a priest). **Murtis** are statues, or small statuettes of the gods. They are available (as are posters) from Hindu temples and educational suppliers. They may show variations of the objects and animals associated with the deities, representing the variations on the stories associated with each deity.

Brahma is the creator.

Shiva (the Lord of the Dance) shown performing his cosmic dance, is the destroyer.

Vishnu is the preserver (see page 10, Creation).

Activities

- The children should notice the following features of the gods.

God	Arms and hands	Head and face	Objects	Creatures
Vishnu	Four arms. Each hand holds something.	A mark on his forehead. ◊	a conch shell a discus a mace a lotus flower	a snake
Brahma	Four arms. Each hand holds something.	Four heads. A mark on his forehead. ২৫	prayer beads a spoon a water pot a book	a swan
Shiva	Two hands hold things, one is held up and one points.	A mark on his forehead and one on his neck. III	a drum fire	a snake a demon

- Share this story with the children:
  'Shiva, Brahma and Vishnu argued about who was the greatest. A column of light appeared and they had a competition to see who could reach the end of it first. Brahma flew upwards as a goose, Vishnu became a boar and dived downwards. As they moved the column grew; it had no ends. Shiva's voice came from the centre of the pillar, saying, "I am Shiva, the great god. All forms are forms of me." A pillar is often used as a symbol for Shiva.'
- The children could draw the story in pictures.

Developments

- The children could draw themselves in different situations and with different expressions on their faces. They could talk about the different ways in which they behave: gently, calmly, aggressively, angrily and so on. Link this with discussion of the different forms of god.
- To develop an understanding of symbolism, ask the children to depict themselves as an animal that shows how they would like to be seen. What does the animal suggest? Strength? Wisdom? Speed?

Hindu deities

Hindus worship God in many forms.

● Talk to a friend about what is special about these gods.

'They call him Indra, Mitra, Varuna, Agni or the heavenly sunbird, Garutman.
The seer calls in many ways that which is one.'
Rig Veda 1, !6:46

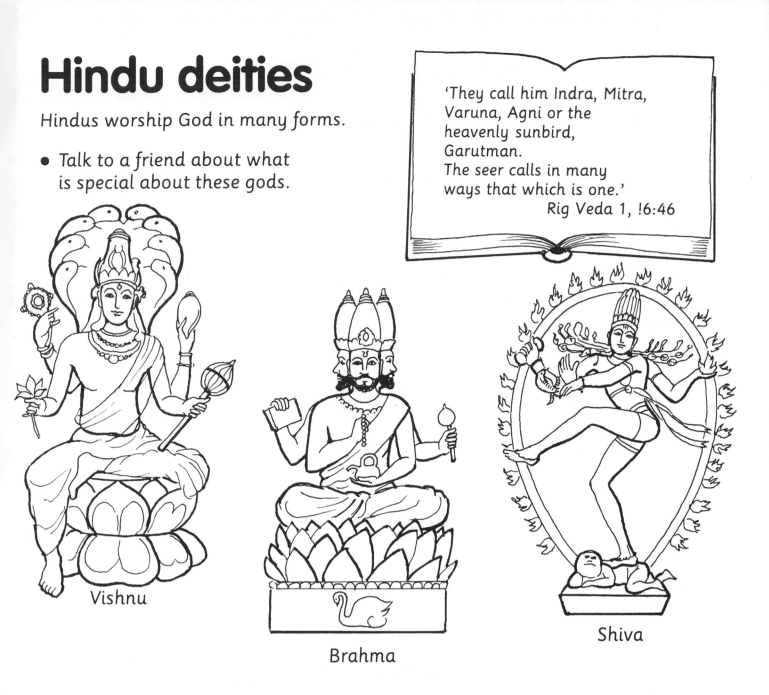

Vishnu

Brahma

Shiva

● Use this chart to describe the gods.

God	Arms and hands	Head and face	Objects	Creatures

 ● What can you find out about the gods' characters?

Goddesses – Ideas Page

Aim

- Appreciating the significance of female deities, and that deities are worshipped according to how well their characteristics match the needs of the worshipper.

Activities

- The children could list and analyse the many tasks that God has to do to manage the business of looking after the Universe. What different forms might God have to take to do these tasks?

Managing the Universe		
Job	Skills and Knowledge	Character
Fighting Evil	Using weapons quick reactions	brave strong
Looking after weak, sick or disabled people.	Medicine	kind patient

- The children could consider the tasks from their 'Running the Universe' chart, deciding whether they could be done by a man or a woman or either, explaining their reasons.
- *Activity sheet answers:*
  Saraswati – She is the goddess of learning. Children pray to her for help at school.
  Lakshmi – People pray to her when they need help with money. She is the goddess of good fortune.
  Durga – She is a brave warrior. She is ready to do many jobs and will fight if she has to.
- With research, the children could match the goddesses to some of the tasks.

Background

In many Hindu traditions the goddess, or devi, is thought of as the strength and protector of mothers and children, or even the **shakti** or strength and power behind all things in the Universe. **Durga**, **Parvati** and **Kali** are different forms of the same goddess. As Durga (see **Navaratri**, pages 42–43) she is a brave ten-armed warrior who rides on a tiger. As Kali she appears in a frightening and ugly form that wears a necklace of skulls. She is the bringer of war, quarrels and disease. As Parvati she is gentle and beautiful, the mother of **Ganesha**, the elephant god (pages 20–21).

Parvati

Kali

Lakshmi, the partner of **Vishnu**, is the goddess of good fortune, and **Saraswati**, the partner of **Brahma**, is the goddess of wisdom and learning. She plays a stringed musical instrument called a vina.

Developments

- Draw the children's attention to some of the symbolism of the deities. They are often portrayed with many arms, symbolising power. The glory of God is portrayed in their richly decorated clothes and jewellery.
- The children may be able to draw conclusions about the nature of a god or goddess from the position of the hands. They can draw from their own experience of using their hands to express messages such as:

comforting   granting a wish

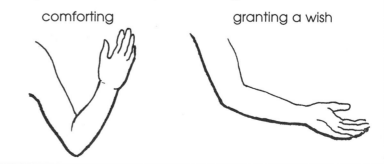

IDEAS BANK – *Hinduism*

Goddesses

Hindus worship God in male and female forms.
Each goddess is special in a different way.

'Into the bosom of the one great sea
Flow streams from hill on every side.
Their names are various as the springs
And people in every land bow down
To one Great God, known by many names.'

Indian folk song.

- Match the sentences to the pictures.

She is a brave warrior.	People pray to her when they need help with money.	She is the goddess of learning.

Saraswati   Durga   Lakshmi

She is the goddess of good fortune.	Children pray to her for help at school.	She is ready to do many jobs and will fight if she has to.

- Explain to a friend how you matched the sentences to the pictures.

- Which goddess might these Hindus worship:

a soldier? _____   a shopkeeper? _____   a teacher? _____

IDEAS BANK – *Hinduism*

Creation – Ideas Page

Aim

- Awareness of the Hindu creation story and the belief in a deity who is a creator and protector.

Background

The Hindu faith includes three aspects of **Brahman**, the one true God: **Brahma**, the creator, **Vishnu**, the preserver and **Shiva**, the destroyer (pages 6–7). Destroying in this sense is not seen as negative because Hindus believe in the continuous cycle of existence: birth, death and reincarnation. Therefore, death is an essential part of creation. The hymn of creation on the activity sheet is from the **Rig Veda**, one of the Hindu holy books.

Activities

- Begin by asking the children to imagine what it was like before the world was created. They could close their eyes and think of sounds and smells, what they can feel and what they can see. Written descriptions could be presented with the children's paintings, to produce a display.
- After they have completed the activity sheet, ask them to describe or draw what happened to the world once there were people in it.

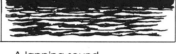

Before the world began

Everywhere was dark. There was just water and empty space.

A lapping sound swished and buzzed over the water.

A cool breeze blew. It smelled like the beach.

Developments

- Can the children explain why there should be a god that destroys? What would they decide to destroy or preserve in the world? Consider resources that are 'destroyed' or killed in order to create something new: trees for furniture and paper, ores for metal.

Buddha, the teacher.

Parasurama, the warrior who put an end to war.

Kalki, the slayer who will destroy evil.

Kuma, the tortoise who helped the gods become immortal.

- Collect and display books and pictures that show the ten avatars of Vishnu (the ten forms in which he appeared on the Earth). The other six not shown here are: Matsya, the fish that saved the creatures of the world in the great flood; **Krishna**, the cowherd; **Rama**

(pages 26–27); Vamana, the beautiful dwarf; Narasimha, who was half-man and half-lion and killed a demon; Varaha the boar who saved the Earth when it fell from its place.

- In Hindu belief, Vishnu came to Earth in one of these forms whenever he was needed and still intervenes whenever humankind needs him, creating good where there is evil.
- The children could look at pictures of Shiva with his cosmic fire (pages 6–7) and explain how fire can be seen as something that creates as well as destroys. This will be easier if fire is linked to heat – the heat of the Sun helps plants grow and in the Hindu faith (pages 36–37) the fire of the funeral pyre purifies.

Creation

Hindus believe that Brahma created the Universe.
This is the Hindu story of creation.

'Then neither Being nor Not-Being was,
Nor air, nor Earth, nor what is beyond.
What did it surround? Where? In whose protection?
What was water, the deep, the unfathomable.'

Hymn of creation, Rig Veda.

It's time to create the world

Yes, my Lord

Before time began Vishnu slept on the coiled snake, Shesha, floating on the vast sea. A humming sound began, 'A – U – M.'

The vibrations woke Vishnu and a beautiful lotus flower grew from his navel. Brahma sat in the middle of the lotus.

Brahma calmed the sea. He created the Earth, sky and heavens from the lotus.

Brahma filled the Earth with living things.

- Draw the next picture for the story. ⟶

NOW

- With friends, plan how you will enact this story. Think about the sounds, 'props' and clothes you might use.

IDEAS BANK – *Hinduism*

Mahatma Gandhi – Ideas Page

Aim

- Awareness of the importance of Gandhi as a faith leader and of the Hindu belief in **ahimsa** (non-violence).

Activities

- The activity page may be used to introduce work on Gandhi. Working in pairs, the children could discuss their ideas of what they would have done in Gandhi's position.
- He actually spent the night on the railway platform. In that time he resolved to follow the principles described in box A on the activity sheet.

- Present-day examples of ahimsa may be found in the news or even in the school. Have the children seen victims of abuse and name-calling walk away from this without fighting back? What does this tell them about the victims and the name-callers?
- The children could try writing their own 'ahimsa' stories.

Background

Gandhi grew up in India, worshipping God in the form of **Vishnu**. He studied law in London when he was nineteen, but was always interested in religion and read both the Bible and the **Bhagavad Gita**. His job was in South Africa and it was here that he met apartheid. This experience made him resolve to fight against racial prejudice and injustice, while still following the Hindu belief in ahimsa. Ahimsa, a belief in non-violence, also extends to animals and consequently most Hindus are vegetarian.

The Hindu caste system (see page 14) included the untouchables. Gandhi saw this as unjust and taught people that to think of people as untouchable was racial prejudice, that the untouchables were God's children and that they should be welcomed into temples. He also fought for India's right to govern itself, independent from British rule, but through peaceful methods. Even though some of Gandhi's protests led to him being put in prison, they were often successful in bringing change.

Gandhi encouraged peaceful protest against racial segregation and British rule in India.

Developments

- Collect and display books about Gandhi. Ask the children to research incidents from the life of Gandhi that show his belief in ahimsa and satyagraha (standing up for one's rights). They could work in groups to enact these incidents.

Mahatma Gandhi

Mohandas Karamchand Gandhi was born in 1869 in Porbandar, India.

An Indian poet, Rabindranath Tagore, gave him the name 'Mahatma'. It means 'Great soul'.

One day Gandhi was travelling in South Africa:

'There is peace in the heavenly region;
There is peace in the atmosphere, peace reigns on the Earth;
There is coolness in the water; the medicinal waters are healing;
The plants are peace-giving;
There is harmony in the celestial objects;
There is perfection in eternal knowledge;
Everything in the Universe is peaceful; peace is everywhere.
May that peace come to me!'
　　Part of the Shanti Path – Hymn of Peace.

First class is for white people only. Please move to the third class carriage.

No, I have a first-class ticket.

FIRST CLASS
—
WHITES ONLY

It is the law. If you do not obey it, you must get off the train.

- What would you have done if you were Gandhi?

_____

_____

- Read Box A.
- What do you think Gandhi did?

_____

_____

_____

_____

A
Gandhi practised satyagraha, which means standing up for what you think is right.
　　He also practised ahimsa, which means 'love that operates through non-violence'. He believed in peaceful protest.

NOW • Describe a present-day example of ahimsa.

Brahmin – Ideas Page

Aim

- Understanding the role of the priest as a faith leader in the local community and of his position in society as a member of the first varna or division of Hindu society.

Activities

- Explain that the **murtis** (statues of deities) are treated as if they are living deities. Each morning the priest washes and dresses them in ornate clothing and each evening reverses the process (some do this weekly), preparing them for sleep. Pages 22–23 give details of puja.
- The children could plan for a speaker to visit their class – perhaps a local Hindu priest.
- The children could also use planning-charts to show how they will make the visitor welcome and what they will offer him/her in hospitality :

Name of visitor _____
Date of visit _____
Time of visit _____
Meeting the visitor:
Receptionist : _____
Refreshment _____
Who will introduce the visitor?
_____
Who will thank him or her?
_____
What will he or she say?
_____
_____

Background

The occupations of Hindus are still greatly influenced by the **varna**, or group to which their family belongs. The caste system derives from this. There were four main varnas in ancient India:

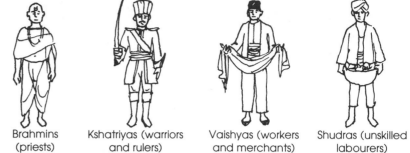

Brahmins (priests)   Kshatriyas (warriors and rulers)   Vaishyas (workers and merchants)   Shudras (unskilled labourers)

Today people from all varnas celebrate all the main festivals, but at one time particular festivals were associated with individual varnas. For example, only **brahmins** would celebrate **Raksha Bandhan** (pages 16–17). However, only the first three varnas are meant to celebrate the sacred thread ceremony (page 34), and in practice usually only brahmins do so. The caste system is dying out in India but most Hindus know to which caste they belong. Many surnames, as well as occupations, are linked to caste.

Developments

- Collect and display photographs, posters and descriptions of brahmins, showing the activities that take place in a Hindu temple, as described on the pupil page.
- The children should notice the markings on the brahmin's forehead, showing the deity that he worships. The sacred thread is first worn at the **upanayana samskar** (sacred thread ceremony). At one time this marked the investiture of the student or a serious approach to study. Nowadays it bears no real relation to education. Many Hindu parents ensure that the ceremony is carried out before their sons marry.

A brahmin

Visiting speakers

- Internationally-renowned holy people and those with knowledge of particular aspects of Hinduism visit Hindu temples throughout the world to speak to the Hindu community. These important visits are usually organised by the priest.
- If possible arrange for a Hindu priest to talk to the children about his work.
- The children could then work out the priest's daily routine, deciding what special characteristics, knowledge and understanding are necessary for this role.

Brahmin

The brahmin (priest) is in charge of worship in the temple. The pictures and captions show some of his work.

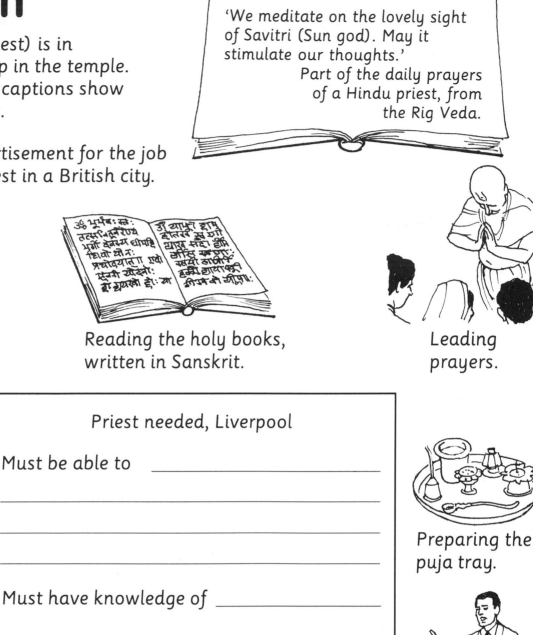

'We meditate on the lovely sight of Savitri (Sun god). May it stimulate our thoughts.'
Part of the daily prayers of a Hindu priest, from the Rig Veda.

● Write an advertisement for the job of a Hindu priest in a British city.

Collecting offerings.

Reading the holy books, written in Sanskrit.

Leading prayers.

Looking at star charts to choose a name for a baby.

Priest needed, Liverpool

Must be able to _____

_____

_____

_____

Must have knowledge of _____

_____

_____

_____

Character _____

_____

_____

Preparing the puja tray.

Looking after the murtis.

Inviting holy people to give talks at the temple.

NOW ● Find out more about the work of Hindu priests.

● Write a job description for a priest, showing his working hours.

IDEAS BANK – *Hinduism*

Brothers and sisters –

Aim

- Understanding the importance of family ties in Hinduism and the significance of knots as symbols.

Developments

- Collect and display gifts and cards that are specially designed for members of families to give to each other – 'brother', 'sister', Mothers' Day, Fathers' Day and Grandparents' Day cards.
- The children could classify the cards, noting the items depicted and the colours used.
- Before writing a Raksha Bandhan verse for a girl to give to a brother or cousin, the children could explore the meaning of 'family ties'. They could list the ways in which members of a family can help each other.
- Use commercially-made Raksha Bandhan cards to draw the children's attention to the symbols used – knots and rakhis – before they design their own cards.

Background

In Hinduism, knots symbolise the strength of family relationships (pages 30–31 and 34–35). These knots are untied with great care and often prayers, to emphasise concern for preventing broken relationships.

Raksha Bandhan means 'tie of protection'. Girls and women tie **rakhis** to their brothers' wrists, or if they have no brothers, to male cousins' or other male relatives' wrists, asking for their help and protection. They receive a present in return, often sweets. The rakhi is usually tied to the right wrist. The custom, which takes place in the home, rather than the temple, is continued after brothers and sisters are married, to reinforce family bonds.

A legend associated with Raksha Bandhan tells of when King Bali drove Indra, the King of Heaven, from his home. Sacha, the wife of Indra asked **Vishnu** to help her to regain her husband's kingdom and to keep him safe. Vishnu gave her an amulet to tie around Indra's right wrist before he fought Bali. Indra had great faith in the protection of Vishnu's amulet and managed to defeat Bali and regain his kingdom.

Activities

- Ask the children, in groups, to discuss and make a note of anything that comes to mind when they think of brothers, sisters or cousins. They could list the advantages and disadvantages of having a brother, sister or cousin.

Having a brother	
Advantages	Disadvantages
There is always someone to play with. Company on holidays.	He uses my felt tips. He eats my sweets. He reads my diary.

- Can the children explain how brothers and sisters are different from friends (apart from being blood relations)? What is special about being a brother or sister?
- The children could display their rakhis, labelling them to show who will receive them and what they will wish for them.

Brothers and sisters

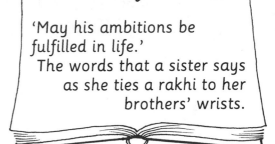

'May his ambitions be fulfilled in life.'
The words that a sister says as she ties a rakhi to her brothers' wrists.

At Raksha Bandhan, Hindu girls and women tie rakhis to their brothers' wrists.

● Make a rakhi.

1. Punch two holes in the card circle.

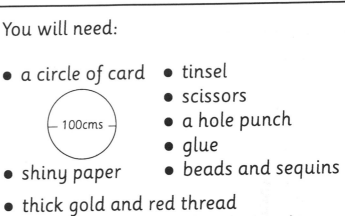

You will need:

● a circle of card
● shiny paper
● thick gold and red thread
(the sort used for gift wrapping)

● tinsel
● scissors
● a hole punch
● glue
● beads and sequins

100cms

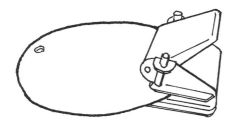

2. Decorate it with tinsel.

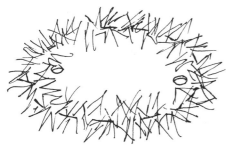

3. Stick on flower shapes made from shiny paper.

4. Make a pattern with beads and sequins.

5. Make two plaits, about 30cm long, from red and gold thread.

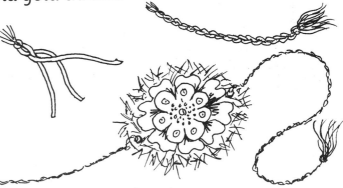

6. Tie the plaits to the card circle.

NOW

● Make up a verse for a sister to give to a brother at Raksha Bandhan.

● Think about the ties between brothers and sister and how they might express affection and good wishes.

The mandir – *Ideas Page*

Aim

- Understanding how the design of a mandir helps Hindus to worship.

Activities

- Collect and display pictures of buildings that are suited to their purpose: supermarkets, hospitals, police stations and so on. Can the children identify them? How? Ask them to identify useful features – signs, maps, trolleys, checkouts and waiting rooms.
- Show the children pictures of Hindu temples. Ask them how they can tell it is a temple.
- Draw their attention to the prayer, noting that it is addressed to one god. Ask them how the different parts of the temple might help the worshippers to forget everyday things and concentrate on worship.
- The activity sheet may be used in conjunction with a visit to a mandir. The children could look for the features shown.
- A temple dedicated to **Shiva** would have not only Shiva's statue, but also that of his partner, **Parvati** (pages 8–9). Shiva's animal is the bull, Nandi, whose statue may be seen in the courtyard.

A

C

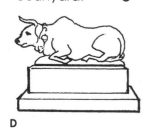

D

Background

Hindu temples (mandirs) are homes of particular deities rather than centres for congregational worship. The most holy part of the **mandir** is the shrine room, where the **murtis** (statues) and pictures of the deities are kept. As the prayer quoted on the activity page shows, Hindus worship one god, each murti reminding them of his presence in a particular form.

As worshippers enter the mandir, they may ring a bell to alert the deity that they are about to worship. They leave offerings of food, flowers and money at the shrine, moving around the temple in a clockwise direction. (See also pages 14–15.)

The shrine of a temple dedicated to **Durga**.

Developments

- The entrance to a mandir has an important function. It helps worshippers to leave behind everyday concerns and to focus on worship. Ask the children to think of ways that they could alter the entrance to the school hall or their classroom, to draw people's attention away from everyday things and prepare them for thinking about God. For example, they could decorate the doorway with intricately-patterned garlands, lotus flower shapes and leaves cut from shiny paper.

- Can the children think of other special ways that people mark doorways for religious reasons? For example, a mezuzah, on the top right-hand doorpost of a Jewish home, which people touch and ask for a blessing as they pass by.

The mandir

Many Hindu mandirs (temples) outside India are converted houses, churches or other buildings.

The diagram below shows a purpose-built temple.

- Match the labels and descriptions to the parts of the temple.

'O Lord of the Universe, supreme soul, dispeller of sorrow, hail to you! May your rule of righteousness be established everywhere, for you banish in an instant the agonies of those who worship you...'
   Part of the arti prayer, said while the arti lamp is moved in circles in front of the murti.

entrance

shrine

stone sculpture of an animal

prayer hall

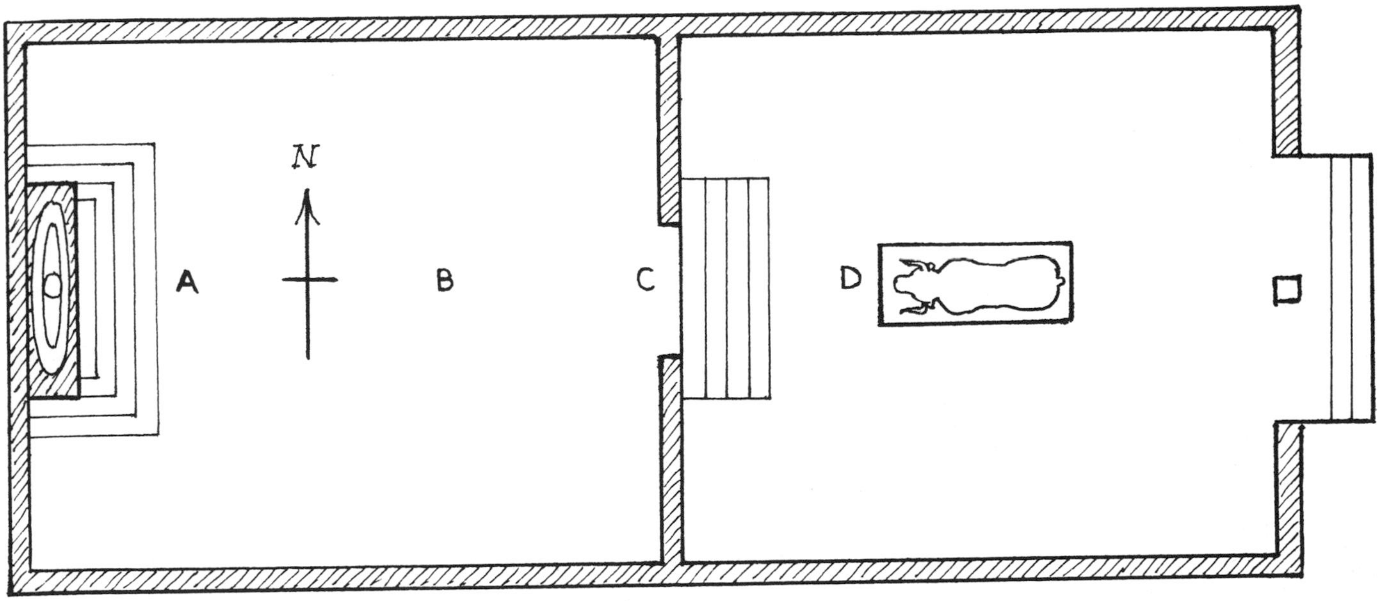

| Where people worship, alone or in groups. | The home of the deities, where their statues and pictures are kept. | The statue of the creature on which the deity rides. | Where people pass through into the prayer hall. |

- Draw the parts labelled a, b and c for a temple dedicated to Shiva. Remember to find out which goddess would be seen with Shiva.

IDEAS BANK – Hinduism

A roadside shrine –

Aims

- Appreciation of what is meant by 'a holy place' and understanding that Hindus can worship in any place that has been made holy by the provision of a picture or statue of a deity.
- Knowledge of the story of **Ganesha** and his importance in Hindu worship.

Activities

- The children will be able to appreciate the symbolism in the picture of Ganesha if they know his story (see *Folens Religious Education, Book 1*):

'**Parvati**, the wife of Shiva, longed for a child, but Shiva was usually away from home. She made Ganesha from flakes of her own skin and breathed life into him. She asked Ganesha to guard the home while she took a bath. Shiva returned home and tried to enter the house. "Keep out," said Ganesha, to Shiva's astonishment. Who could this fat young boy be? "Get out of my way," said Shiva, drawing his sword, but Ganesha bravely fought him. Shiva struck off Ganesha's head. As it lay on the ground, Parvati came out. "You have killed our son," she screamed. Shiva, full of remorse, said that he would find a new head for Ganesha, the head of the next animal that he saw – an elephant.'

- Ask the children to find out what Hindus believe is special about elephants.

Background

Roadside shrines carved from stone or wood are common in India. Worshippers mark the **murti** with **kum kum** (red powder), make offerings of food and flowers and offer prayers as they pass by, for example on their way to work.

Ganesha, god of good fortune and remover of obstacles, is a popular figure for these shrines. He has the body of a fat boy and the head of an elephant. (Elephants are considered holy by Hindus.) His hands may hold a bowl of sweets to reward those who have overcome ignorance (and because he likes sweet things). He may also carry a hatchet to destroy ignorance and a tusk that he broke off to throw at the moon to put out its light when it mocked him (or to replace a broken pen with which he was writing). He wears a sacred thread (pages 14–15) and has prayer beads. His hand position signifies 'Do not fear' and his companion is a rat. The cobra around his waist is a reminder of his father **Shiva**, who is always seen with a snake.

Developments

- Ask the children to describe places by roadsides that people have made special, for worship or to remember people.

Statue of the Virgin Mary   Anfield Memorial

Special Roadside Places		
Place	Description	Purpose
Newross, Republic of Ireland	Statue of the Virgin Mary	For some Christians to worship
St. Malo, France	Cross	Some Christians pray here
Liverpool, England	Anfield Memorial	To remember people who died at a football match.

- The children could create a place that is special for them. Ask them to draw plans for it. What will they put in it? They may choose pictures or objects that remind them of something or someone that they are fond of. Some children may choose a religious theme. How will they decorate it? They may choose flowers or their own drawings. How would they keep it special?
- Hindus remove their shoes before entering a shrine room. Ask the children to devise rules for entering their special place.

A roadside shrine

Hindu worship can take place anywhere that is holy.

A statue or picture of a deity shows that a place is holy.

The god of this roadside shrine is Ganesha.

'Hail Ganesha, hail Ganesha,
Hail Lord Ganesha
Your mother is Parvati,
Your father is Mahadeva (Shiva).'
                    A prayer to Ganesha.

Feature	Description
head	
forehead	
body	
companion	
objects carried	
hand position	
what he wears	

- What can you find out about Ganesha from the picture? Complete the chart.

- What sort of deity is Ganesha? Explain your answer. _____

_____

_____

- Find out more about Ganesha. Explain the symbols that he wears or carries.

The home shrine –

Aim

- To develop understanding of **puja** as worship and of the symbolic use of the articles on the puja tray.

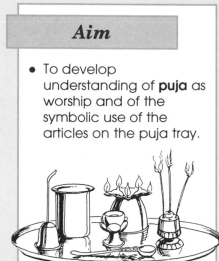

Background

Most Hindu homes have a shrine. Worship is an expression of devotion to deities chosen by the family. It may be addressed to different deities at different times, for example **Saraswati**, when someone is studying for examinations. Worshippers usually bathe, put on clean clothes (but no shoes), ring the bell to wake the gods, light incense sticks and wipe the pictures of the gods and the **murtis** (statues) with water, as if bathing them. The forehead of each god is marked with **kum kum**, and sweets, fruit, water and possibly leaves and flowers are offered to the gods. Then **arti** is performed. This involves lighting the diva and moving the hands above the flame before moving them over the forehead to show that the blessing of god is being received. Great emphasis is placed on purity for worship and leaving behind everyday concerns.

Activities

- Begin by asking the children to remember special occasions and how they prepared for them. What special things did they do? They may have taken special care with cleanliness, brushing their hair, wearing their best clothes. They may have prepared mentally, imagining the occasion. Did they mark off the days on a calendar or count the days?

Prashad

Ingredients:
85g ground rice.
55g ghee (clarified butter)
30g castor sugar.
Optional flavourings may be added: a few drops of vanilla or almond essence.
Rub the ingredients together. When they are thoroughly mixed, make the mixture into a ball and roll it out to a thickness of 1cm on a floured surface. Press it into a baking tray and bake it for 15-20 minutes, or until golden brown, in a hot oven (200°C). Cut it into squares while warm. Leave it to cool on a wire rack.

⚠️ Very close supervision is needed

- If possible show the children a puja tray with the articles shown on the activity page. Encourage them to observe each item using the appropriate senses. They should notice the brightness of the lamp, the red kum kum powder, the smell of the incense, the sound of the bell, the taste of any offerings. **Prashad** is made from ghee (clarified butter), sugar and rice. It is offered to the deities and then shared out between the worshippers.

Developments

- The children could work in groups to produce food for a special occasion, for example to celebrate the achievements of the class.
- Provide simple recipes for the children. (The recipes need not necessarily involve the children having to cook.)
- Ask them to think of how they could present the food to make it look really special.
- Challenge the children to make decorative containers. Who would they invite to share their celebration?

The home shrine

The puja tray is an important part of the family shrine.

- Match the labels to the objects on the puja tray.

bell [ ]

diva lamp [ ]

incense stick holder [ ]

kum kum powder [C]

water pot [B]

spoon [ ]

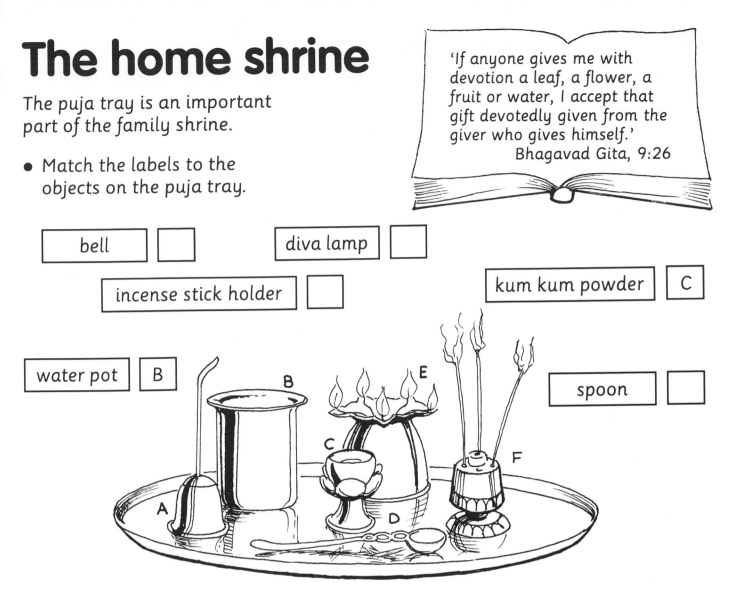

- Match the descriptions to the objects.

To wake the god. [ ]

To put red marks on the foreheads of the god and people to symbolise good health. [ ]

An offering to the god and to wash the statue or picture of the god. A symbol of purity. [ ]

Used to offer milk or water to the god and people. [ ]

To symbolise enlightenment (knowledge of what is good). [ ]

To make a pleasant smell that soothes and cools. [ ]

- Which of your senses is connected with which objects?

 • Why is it important for Hindus to use the puja items to prepare for prayer?

IDEAS BANK – Hinduism

Pilgrimage –

Aims

- Awareness of the significance of pilgrimage with regard to reincarnation.
- Knowledge of pilgrimage sites in India.

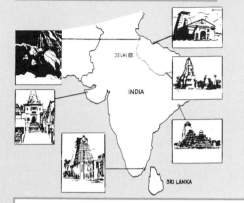

Background

Pilgrimage is important in Hinduism, since life is seen as a journey whose purpose is to find **moksha**, the release of the **atman** (soul) from being reborn and reaching God. Hindus can show devotion to God and try to achieve moksha through pilgrimage. Pilgrimage sites include the source of the holy River **Ganga** and some famous temples.

Many Hindus go to the holy city of Varanasi in their old age to ensure that when they die they can be cremated there and their ashes scattered on the river.

Badrinath, Puri, Dwarka and Rameswaram are the Four Holy Abodes, shrines at the northern, southern, eastern and western extremities of India. At Badrinath is a great temple, housing a giant, jewelled image of **Vishnu**. Pilgrims try to visit Puri in June or July for the car festival, when three images are brought out of the Jagganath temple and taken in huge cars to the nearby **mandir** at Gundicha. Dwarka is holy because it is where **Krishna** ruled as king. Rameswaram is where **Rama** first set foot in India on his return from Lanka (pages 26–27).

Activities

- The children could discuss, then display, places that they have visited, or would like to visit, that are 'special'.

Name	Place	Reason
Emily	Egypt	To see the Pyramids
Geeta	Liverpool	To see the places in the Beatles songs.
Simon	Lapland	The real Father Christmas lives there.
Maria	Denmark	There is a village built from Lego.

- Have they visited places that feel 'special' because of something that has happened there, or someone who has lived there? Ask them to describe anything that they wanted to examine there and what they brought back from the visit.
- If possible, invite a Hindu visitor to talk about a pilgrimage. Collect and display photographs of pilgrimage sites, as well as artefacts such as small statues of deities (available from mandirs or educational suppliers).

Developments

- Provide atlases, books, and travel guides about India. Can the children work out the distance from where they live to one of the pilgrimage sites? They could find out how they would get there, the cost and how long the journey would take.
- Discuss the cost of a pilgrimage in terms of time and money. Many Hindus visit pilgrimage sites as part of a holiday, especially if they are living outside India and return to visit relatives.
- Have the children been on a pilgrimage? Do they know people who have done this? They may make links between pilgrimages in Hinduism and other faiths:

Faith	Site	Significance
Christianity	Lourdes	Vision of Saint Bernadette
	Bethlehem	Birthplace of Jesus
Islam	Makkah	Site of the Ka'bah
Sikhism	Amritsar	Site of the Golden Temple

IDEAS BANK – *Hinduism* © Folens

Pilgrimage

Most Hindus believe that people's souls have to be reborn many times before they find God.

Making a pilgrimage brings people's souls nearer to God.

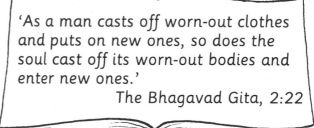
'As a man casts off worn-out clothes and puts on new ones, so does the soul cast off its worn-out bodies and enter new ones.'

The Bhagavad Gita, 2:22

- Link the pictures of pilgrimage sites to their places on the map.

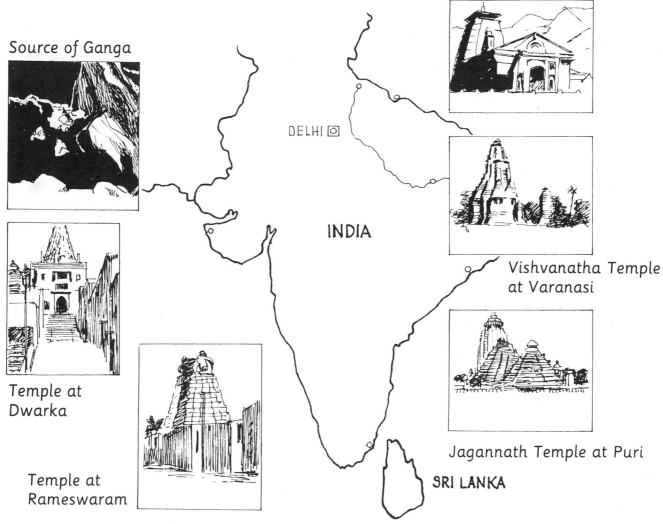

Shrine at Badrinath

Source of Ganga

DELHI

INDIA

Vishvanatha Temple at Varanasi

Temple at Dwarka

Jagannath Temple at Puri

Temple at Rameswaram

SRI LANKA

- Find out more about one of these places.
  Imagine you are a pilgrim there.
- Write a postcard to tell a friend what is special about the place.

The Ramayana – Ideas Page

Aim

- Awareness of the significance of the story of **Rama** and **Sita** as a triumph of good over evil and how the story shows some of the ideals of the Hindu faith.

Activities

- Ask the children to read the picture story. Tell them that Rama's brother, Lakshmana went with Rama and Sita when they were sent away. They could list the good and evil characters in the story. They could look for examples of bravery (the monkeys' willingness to sacrifice their lives for Rama and Sita), and loyalty (Lakshmana did not have to leave Ayodhya, but he stayed with Rama and Sita).

Good	Evil	Not sure
Rama Sita Dasharata Hanuman Lakshmana	Ravana Kaikeyi	Bharata

- Can the children say what the story shows about good and evil?
- Can they think of a famous Hindu man who fought for what he thought was right, and was loyal to his people? (Gandhi, pages 12–13.)
- Ask the children what the story shows about how brothers and sisters should treat each other, reminding them of the festival of **Raksha Bandhan** (pages 16–17).

Background

The **Ramayana** legend tells the story of Rama and Sita and their family. It tells how Rama, with celestial intervention, won the hand of Sita in marriage by winning a competition to string the bow of **Vishnu**, a hitherto impossible feat. The story begins as follows:

'King Dasharata of Ayodhya had three wives, but no children. The god Agni granted Dasharata a magic potion that allowed his wives to bear him children, including his son and heir Rama. While hunting one day, Dasharata accidentally shot a young boy. The boy's parents, a blind couple, died from shock, cursing Dasharata with the words "You will die, like us, grieving for your beloved son." He returned home depressed and frightened, and was wounded in battle. Dasharata's wife Kaikeyi nursed him back to health, encouraging him to fight on and win, which he did. As a reward she could, in the future, demand that he grant her two wishes.' The activity page continues the story.

Developments

- The children could use a planning chart to support their plan for enacting the story:

Enacting the story of Rama and Sita		
Characters	Scenes	
	1 5	
	2 6	
	3 7	
	4 8	
Useful props		

- Collect and display photographs of the giant models of Rama, Sita and Ravana used in Hindu processions during the festival of **Navaratri** (pages 42–43). Note the special characteristics of each character's appearance.

Rama and Sita

The Ramayana

The Ramayana is one of the holy books of Hinduism.

It tells the story of Rama and Sita. It is an epic, a long, exciting story.

'Hari Krishna, Hari Krishna
Hari Rama, Rama, Rama
Krishna Krishna, Hari Hari
Rama Rama, Hari Hari.'
A Hindu chant, often sung at Divali.

With friends, plan how you will enact the story.
Ask your teacher for a planning chart.

The Bhagavad Gita – Ideas Page

Aims

- Awareness of the importance of the **Bhagavad Gita** to Hindus.
- Understanding why it was considered right for Arjuna to go to war against his cousins.

Background

The **Mahabharata** tells the epic tale of the struggle between the Pandavas and the Kauravas, for control of King Dhritarashta's kingdom. The part of it known as the Bhagavad Gita, 'the Song of the Lord', describes the discussion between the god **Krishna** and Arjuna.

Activities

- Tell the children the beginning of the story before they begin the activity sheet:

'King Dhritarashta, who had grown old and blind, decided to hand over his kingdom to his young nephews, the Pandavas. "Send them away," said the furious Kauravas, also nephews of the king, "This kingdom is ours by right." The frightened king did as he was told. The Pandavas hid in a forest, not knowing that the Kauravas planned to burn down their house while they slept. A friend warned them of the plot. "We must disguise ourselves," said one brother. "Yes," agreed Arjuna, "as holy men. Then nobody will recognise us and people will give us food and shelter."

One day a messenger arrived, out of breath. "King Draupada of Panchalas is looking for a husband for his daughter. To win her hand, you must string a mighty bow. Many have tried and failed. You could do it Arjuna." The brothers went to Panchalas with Arjuna, only to find the Kauravas in the competition. When Arjuna easily won and married the princess, the Kauravas became suspicious. "Only Arjuna could do that," said one, "It must be him!"

King Dhritarashta heard the news, guessed who they were and invited the Pandavas back to his palace.'

The story continues on the activity sheet.

King Dhritarashta, who gave away his kingdom to the Pandavas and the Kauravas.

Duryodna of the Kauravas.

Arjuna of the Pandavas.

- The children should consider Arjuna's duty to regain his family's kingdom and his unwillingness to fight his relations. What do they think he did after his discussion with Krishna?

Developments

- Share with the children the outcome of the story:

'Vishnu appeared in the form of Krishna and offered Arjuna and Duryodna (the Kaurava prince) the choice of himself – unarmed – or a huge army to fight with. Arjuna chose Krishna and Duryodna chose the army. Krishna persuaded Arjuna that, although the Kauravas were his cousins, his duty was to fight, because he was a warrior. Arjuna had to do it as an offering to God, not for personal rewards.

Once Arjuna was satisfied that it was indeed right for him to fight, the battle began and the Pandavas won.'

- Can the children explain what the story says about good and evil?

The Bhagavad Gita

The Bhagavad Gita is part of a holy book called the Mahabharata.
The Mahabharata tells the story of a war between two groups of cousins, the Pandavas and the Kauravas.

> 'He who works without attachment, offering his actions to the Supreme, is untouched by sin, as a lotus leaf by water.'
> Bhagavad Gita, 5:10

To get back his family's kingdom, Arjuna would have to fight the Kauravas.

- Explain why he might not want to fight them.

The god Krishna came to persuade Arjuna to do his duty.

- What do you think was his duty?

IDEAS BANK – *Hinduism*

Samskars – Ideas Page

Aims

- Exploring the children's experience of significant events in their own lives.
- Understanding the significance of samskars (sacraments) in Hinduism as milestones in the journey through life.

Background

Hindus view life as a journey, during which people try to reach **Brahman** (God). Life consists of four ashramas (stages):

Brahmachari (student)　　**Grihasti** (householder)　　**Vanaprasthi** (retired)　　**Sannyasin** (renunciate)

The exact origins of the samskars are obscure, but several of the Hindu holy books (page 3) have references to them. Up to 40 samskars have been identified, but 16 are generally accepted.

Samskar	Translation	Purpose	Present-day use
Garbhadana	Conception	Most auspicious timing	Largely abandoned
Pumsavana	Quickening of male child	Asking for a male child	Rare
Simantonnayana	Hair-parting	Protecting a pregnant woman from evil	Rare
Jatakarma	Birth	Long life and intelligence	Replaced by prayers and offerings
Namkara	Name-giving	Giving a name that has good influence	Widespread
Niskarma	First outing	Presenting the child to the gods	Adapted in various ways
Annaprasana	First feeding	Influencing choice of foods	Uncommon
Chudakarana	Hair-cutting	Longevity	Almost universal for boys, less common for girls
Karmavedha	Ear-piercing	Decoration and protection	Common for girls, less so for boys
Vidyarambha	Learning the alphabet	Marking the start of formal education	Rare
Upanayana	Sacred thread	Educational milestone	Widespread
Vedarambha	Studying the Vedas	Marks the start of serious study	Largely abandoned
Kesanta	Shaving	Beginning of manhood	Uncommon
Samavartana	End of studentship	The end of the student ashrama	Combined with Upanayana
Vivaha	Marriage	Entering the ashrama of householder	Widespread
Antyesti	Funeral	Preparing for after-life	Universal

Activities

- The activity sheet provides an introduction to special stages in a person's life. The children could compare their special occasions, noting similarities and differences. Are there any special occasions that are common to everybody?

- Collect and display greetings cards, certificates and other reminders of special occasions. Can the children explain what is special about the occasions?

Developments

- Ask the children to draw pictures or symbols that represent whole stages of their lives:

Baby　　Infant school

Nursery　　Junior school

- Can they continue this for the whole of a person's life (perhaps an adult relation's)?
- Introduce the Hindu ashramas, explaining that each stage prepares for the next and that all prepare a person for meeting God.

Samskars

Samskars are Hindu ceremonies to mark important stages in a person's life.

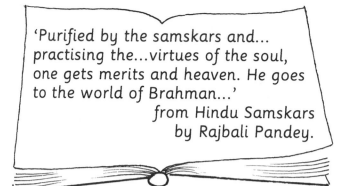

'Purified by the samskars and... practising the...virtues of the soul, one gets merits and heaven. He goes to the world of Brahman...'
from Hindu Samskars by Rajbali Pandey.

- Think of some important events in your life.
- Mark them on the time line. You could draw pictures or symbols on the time line.

▶ 19__

▶ 19__

▶ ___

- What have you kept to remind you of these events?

_____

_____

- Find out about the special events marked by Hindu samskars.

New baby – Ideas Page

Aim

- Understanding the significance of some of the **samskars** (sacraments) associated with birth, naming a child and other important occasions.

Activities

- Provide books for the children to find the meanings of their names. They could draw or paint pictures of themselves showing the characteristics of their names.

Chloe means a young green shoot.

Nicholas means victory of the people

- The children should decide for themselves whether the baby on the activity sheet is a girl or a boy.

Background

There are samskars for 16 significant occasions throughout life. In practise, many Hindus do not regard them as relevant to modern times (pages 30–31 and 34–37).

Hindu customs vary, but usually a priest is involved in selecting a name for a child. He will prepare a horoscope, which will suggest choices of letters or syllables to be included in the name. The temple and family deities also influence the choice of name, as will names of other family members.

The name-giving samskar (**Namkara**) may take place in the home or temple and usually follows **puja** (pages 22–23). Offerings are made to the deities. A priest may be involved, but the child's father performs the naming rite.

Many Hindu mothers mark the baby with a tiny spot of black kohl, often in a place that is out of sight, since black is regarded as an auspicious colour that wards off evil. Also, to ward off evil, a baby's aunt may tie scarlet threads to the baby's cradle and around his or her wrist.

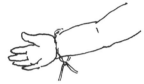

Three other samskars commonly performed for babies are: the first outing (Niskarma), hair-cutting (Chudakarana, usually for boys only) and ear-piercing (Karmavedha, usually for girls only).

Developments

- The children could plan and make a tableau of a Niskarma samskar (first outing for a baby – page 30). Ask them what the baby would see, hear, smell and taste with regards to the puja tray items (pages 22–23). Sounds could include a bell and the syllable **aum** and the smell could be that of incense (with supervision the children could burn different kinds of incense, choosing their favourite smells). The taste could be **prashad** (page 22), or honey with which the symbol aum is sometimes written on the baby's tongue.

Ganesha   Lakshmi   Shiva   Krishna

- They could use coloured paper to make a temple for the background of the tableau. Referring to posters, photographs and small statues, the children could use shiny paper to produce pictures of the deities of the temple.

New baby

Hindu parents usually ask a priest to help them choose the name for a baby.

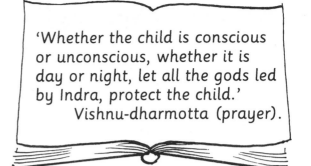

'Whether the child is conscious or unconscious, whether it is day or night, let all the gods led by Indra, protect the child.'
Vishnu-dharmotta (prayer).

Some people believe that a person's name affects his or her life and character.

- What would you wish for this baby? Complete the boxes.

Mind

Body

Character

Talents

- List your eight favourite boys' or girls' names and find their meanings.

NOW

- Imagine the priest has told you that the baby's name must begin with M. Choose a name that you like.

    Its meaning must match your wishes for the baby.

Name	Meaning

Marriage – **Ideas Page**

Aim

- Awareness that symbols are used in ceremonies of many faiths.
- Understanding some of the Hindu wedding symbols.

Activities

- Ask the children to bring in wedding pictures and artefacts, as well as symbols, wedding cards and invitations.
- They could look for symbols. Can they explain what each item might symbolise?
- If possible, display colour photographs and posters and show a Hindu wedding video.
- The children could make flower garlands by threading fresh or artificial flower heads or tissue paper petals.

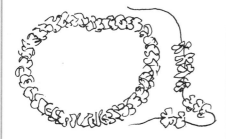

- They could make a pochi (hand jewellery).

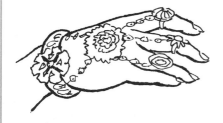

- Activity answers: a) Aum, the most holy Hindu symbol; b) Ganesha, the god who removes obstacles and brings good luck; c) Fire, a symbol of purification; d) Knotted cloth: a symbol that the bride and groom are united for ever; e) Coconut, a holy symbol that may be given as an offering by the bride.

Background

Wedding customs vary between communities. Arranged marriages are common and are usually between couples from a similar social background (**varna** – page 14). Before marriage, a man has usually undergone the **Upanayana** (sacred thread) **samskar**, indicating that he has left the **brahmachari** (student) ashram and is ready to enter the grihasti (householder) ashram. Before the betrothal takes place an astrologer may be consulted to check the compatibility of the partners and to suggest an auspicious day for the wedding.

During the ceremony there may be symbolism of the joining of two families: reading out names of the bride and groom's ancestors, making tilak marks with red paste on the foreheads of each other's family, exchanging of gifts.

The bride is likely to wear a red sari, red being considered a lucky colour.

Developments

- A chart comparing a Hindu wedding with other weddings may develop as follows:

	Buddhist	Christian	Hindu	Jewish	Muslim	Sikh
flowers	✓	✓	✓	✓		
red paste			✓			
sweets			✓			✓
knot			✓			
red			✓			
white		✓				
fire			✓			

- If possible collect some advertisements for brides from newspapers of a Hindu community. Families in some communities may find marriage partners for their sons and daughters in this way. To some children this practice may be alien. They could list the advantages and disadvantages of arranged marriages and those where the partners meet in other ways.

Marriage

People make wishes and promises when they marry.

Hindu weddings have many symbols for these.

'Take one step for securing food. Take two steps for strength, three steps for increase in wealth. Take four steps for happiness. Take five steps for children. Take six steps for seasonal pleasures. Take seven steps as a friend.'
From the Hindu marriage samskar.

- Match each label to part of this Hindu wedding.

| Knotted cloth | |
| Ganesha | |

| Fire | |

| Coconut | |
| Aum | |

BHAVNA

NIMISH

- Match the descriptions to the objects and labels.

The most holy Hindu symbol.

A symbol of purification.

The god who removes obstacles and brings good luck.

This fruit is a holy symbol. The bride may give it as an offering to the deities.

A symbol that the bride and groom are united for ever.

- Find out more about Hindu weddings.
- Make a chart to show differences and similarities between Hindu weddings and other weddings.

When someone dies – Ideas Page

Aim

- Exploring ideas about what happens when people die, the meaning of 'soul', particularly in the Hindu faith.
- Understanding the reasons for parts of the Hindu funeral **samskar**.

Activities

- Provide photographs or real-life examples of pets that have short life-spans, such as hamsters, gerbils, mice or goldfish.
- Have the children had pets that have died? What happened to the animals after they died? The children may be able to describe what they and their families did with the dead pet and anything that was done to help them to remember it.

Background

The **Bhagavad Gita** (pages 3, 28–29) describes the purpose of life as liberation of the soul from its cycle of rebirth to achieve union with God. The funeral **samskar** aids this process. Many Hindus believe that without the correct funeral rites the soul stays in a state of unrest and could even harm the living. Funeral customs vary, but the following sequence is common:

1. Purification before death could entail a visit to Ganga or receiving water from this holy river.

2. The funeral pyre in India is built from carefully chosen wood.

3. The body is wrapped in white cloth and placed in the pyre.

4. Sometimes ghee (clarified butter) and incense are put on the pyre. A close relative lights it.

5. The mourners may wash, sometimes in a river or stream, to purify themselves.

6. The bones or ashes are collected and may be put in Ganga or another river, or buried under a tree.

7. Ten days after the funeral the shraddha ceremony, where special foods are eaten and music played, helps the dead person's soul to travel to Yama, the land of the God of the dead. Useful items for the year-long journey are given to the priest.

Developments

- The idea of rebirth could be developed by looking at a dead tree. The children could think about its life and how parts of it continue to live in other forms, for example new trees have grown from its seeds. Useful poems include *Firewood* by Norman MacCaig, *To a Telegraph Pole* by Louis Untermeyer and *Tree* by Clive Sansom (all in *Shades of Green*, compiled by Anne Harvey, Red Fox).
- Describe a Hindu funeral and the preparation of the dead. Ask the children to look for actions that might help the soul to reach God. Discuss the visits made by many old Hindus to the holy River **Ganga** (pages 24–25). Draw attention to the smoke that rises from the pyre, like the smoke from incense during **puja** (pages 22–23), the placing of bones or ashes in Ganga or another river, and presents of food and other items for a journey that may be passed to the priest during the shraddha ceremony.
- Find books that explore the complex issues of death.

The Day Grandma Died
Dandelion Year
Don't Forget Tom
Badger's Parting Gifts
The Fall of Freddy the Leaf
The Tenth Good Thing about Barney
The Tale of Three Trees
Conker Tree
Remembering Granddad

When someone dies

Most Hindus believe that when people die their souls will be reborn again and again until they are fit to be with God.

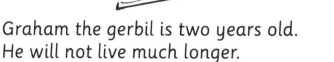

'Just as the soul in this body passes through childhood, youth and old age, so too at death it passes into another body.'

Bhagavad Gita, 11:3

Graham the gerbil is two years old.
He will not live much longer.

- With a friend, plan what you would do when Graham the gerbil dies.

What we would do with the body:	People to include in what we do:
What we would write:	What we would say:
What we would sing:	What will happen to the gerbil afterwards:

- Talk to a friend about what happens to people when they die.

 • Explain what a person's soul is. _____

_____

_____

_____

Festival calendar – Ideas Page

Aim

- Understanding how the Hindu calendar matches the international calendar.

Activities

- Using the completed activity page the children could describe the weather and seasonal conditions in which Hindu festivals take place. Can they suggest why winter is an appropriate time for **Divali** (celebrated on the darkest night of the year)?

- Using their completed calendar, the children could find out during which months of the international calendar (and which season) Hindus in Britain celebrate the festivals listed. How is this different from in India?
- They should be able to work out when Hindus celebrate New Year (Annakuth), as they can see that the first month of the year is Karttik. They could also use the Hindu calendar to write the date.

Background

The Hindu calendar is lunar, and each month has a 'dark half' and a 'light half'. Different calendars are used in different parts of India. Further complication is added by the fact that the timing of some of the festivals is solar. The Hindu calendar corresponds approximately to the international (Gregorian) calendar (see activity sheet). The six seasons of the Indian year are:

Hindu season	Type of season	Hindu months
Basanta	Spring	Phalgun, Chaitra
Grishma	Summer	Vaisakhi, Jayshyth
Varsha	Rainy season	Ashadh, Shravan
Sharad	Autumn	Bhadrapad, Ashvin
Hemant	Winter	Karttik, Agrahayan*
Shishir	Dewy (Cool season)	Paush, Magh

*On some calendars Agrahayan is called Margashisura.

Different regions of India have slightly altered season-month correlations, for example spring may consist of the months of Chaitra and Vaisakhi, which means that the months of all the other seasons are altered: summer would be Jayshyth and Ashadh and so on.

Days of the week are: Somavar (Monday), Mangalvar (Tuesday), Budhvar (Wednesday), Brahaspativar (Thursday), Sukraar (Friday), Sanivar (Saturday) and Ravivar (Sunday). These spellings vary from one source to another, because there are not always exact phonetic equivalents in English.

Developments

- The children could list any festivals that they have celebrated or will celebrate during the current year against each month.
- They could combine all the festivals listed on their charts to make a full year's calendar as a large wall display, marking on it and adding illustrations of festivals celebrated by each child in the class. This could form an ongoing project that the children could add to over a few weeks.

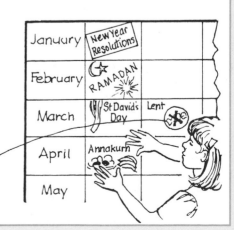

Festival calendar

A pattra is a special calendar that matches up months of the Hindu year with the months of a January to December calendar.

- Mark the centre circle January to December.
- Write the Hindu months in the next circle, in their correct places.
- One has been done for you.

Hindu months	International calendar
Chaitra	March-April
Vaisakhi	April-May
Jayshyth	May-June
Ashadh	June-July
Shravan	July-Aug
Bhadrapad	Aug-Sept
Ashvin	Sept-Oct
Karttik	Oct-Nov
Agrahayan	Nov-Dec
Paush	Dec-Jan
Magh	Jan-Feb
Phalgun	Feb-March

Key	
D	Divali
H	Holi
J	Janmashtami
N	Navaratri

NOW
- Find the names of the six seasons of the Indian year and write these in the outer circle.
- Using the key, see how many Hindu festivals you can label on the calendar.

IDEAS BANK – Hinduism

Janmashtami – Ideas Page

Aim

- Exploring the significance of the birth of **Krishna** (as an incarnation of Vishnu) and the ways in which it is celebrated by Hindus.

Activities

- Provide pictures and, if possible, small statues of Krishna and Radha. Can the children explain the significance of any of the symbols or artefacts, in relation to the story of Krishna's birth and childhood?

A statue of Krishna and Radha

- Groups of children could produce large drawings or paintings of scenes from the story, to form a classroom display. They could add captions and speech bubbles, selecting the appropriate typefaces and print sizes on a word processor.

Background

Many Hindus believe Krishna to be an **avatar** or incarnation of **Vishnu** (pages 6, 7 and 10). These avatars appeared on the Earth whenever people needed guidance as to how they should live.

The story continues from the activity sheet with how Yashoda and Nanda (friends of Krishna's parents) looked after him as he grew up. He spent most of his time playing with the gopis (the girls who looked after cows), making mischief by hiding their clothes while they were bathing and eating their butter and cream. Krishna was always forgiven because of his happy nature and his ability to charm everyone with the beautiful music he played on his flute. He also performed heroic deeds, saving people from harm. They knew he must be a god. Meanwhile, Kansa hunted for Krishna and eventually lured him out of hiding by arranging an athletics competition. As Krishna travelled through a forest, he was attacked by ogres and demons sent by Kansa, but Krishna overcame them all and eventually came face to face with Kansa himself. There was a fierce battle, but Krishna killed Kansa, ridding the world of evil. He married Radha, one of the gopis.

Janmashtami celebrates Krishna's birth and occurs on the eighth day of the dark half of Bhadrapad (pages 38–39). Parties are held in the home and a cradle holding a Krishna doll is often made. Cords attached to the cradle allow children to take it in turns to rock the baby Krishna.

Developments

- The children could set up a corner of the classroom to resemble Janmashtami celebrations. They should be aware that while they are not being asked to take part in an act of worship, they should handle the artefacts with reverence.
- Can the children think of important people connected with religious beliefs? They could display their ideas on a chart:

Key Figures	Faith
Jesus	Christianity
Moses	Judaism
Muhammad	Islam
Siddartha Guatama	Buddhism
Guru Nanak	Sikhism
Saint Bernadette	Christianity

Janmashtami

Many Hindus believe that God was born on Earth, as Krishna, to destroy evil.

Janmashtami is the celebration of Krishna's birth.

'Vasudeva saw that wonderful child of lotus-like eyes, endowed with four arms, bearing a conch and a necklace, a mace, a discus and a lotus.'
Bhagavad Purana 10, 3:9–10

- Explain to a friend how Krishna was still in danger.

- Find out what happened next and continue the picture story.

Aims

- Exploring the idea of a Mother Goddess.
- Appreciation of the joyful festival feeling of Navaratri and links with the goddess (in particular Durga).

Activities

- Provide pictures of the male deities so that the children can work out the donors of some of the things carried by Durga: Shiva – trident, Vishnu – the discus, Brahma – the beads.
- The children could paint pictures of the battle.

Background

Navaratri is celebrated on the first ten days (nine nights) of the light half of Ashvin (pages 44–45). **Durga** is commonly worshipped as the creative power of the divine (**shakti**), and **Lakshmi** and **Kali** may be worshipped to a lesser extent.

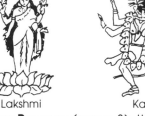

Durga   Lakshmi   Kali

The story of Durga is told in the **Puranas** (page 3). It tells of a buffalo-demon, Mahshasura, who gained **Brahma's** favour. Brahma proclaimed that no male warrior could destroy Mahshasura. The demon assumed that no woman could defeat him and even began to attack Brahma. The gods asked **Shiva** for help. In his anger, a beam of light shone from Shiva's eyes, then from the eyes of the other gods. The beams fused together and there in the middle was the ten-armed goddess, Durga. The gods gave her weapons and a tiger arrived for her to ride on into battle with the demon. Mahshasura mocked Durga, but she opened her mouth and out marched an enormous army.

Developments

- The stick dance is traditionally performed during Navaratri. The children could try this. They will need two sticks, called dandyas, made by decorating 40cm lengths of bamboo or broom handle in bright colours.

1. Practise hitting the sticks to a rhythm while walking, to begin with on every beat. If possible, use traditional Indian music, available from educational suppliers.

2. Make a circle and walk in rhythm, hitting the sticks on the first and third beats.

3. Move clockwise for eight beats, then change direction.

4. Practise this, adding a pivot and dip on the left foot to change direction when moving clockwise and vice-versa when moving anti-clockwise. Do this while beating the stick on each eighth beat.

- The stick dance is often performed around a **madh**, a special six-sided shrine to the goddess. The children could make a model of a madh:

NET FOR A MADH

TABS

BASE

PICTURE OF THE GODDESS

Navaratri

Navaratri means nine nights. It is a celebration of the Mother Goddess.

The gods gave Durga special weapons with which to fight the demon Mahshasura.

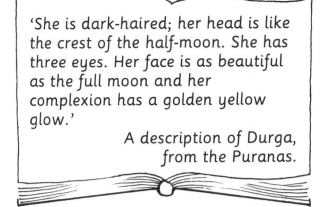

● Draw lines to label the things that Durga is carrying in her ten hands.

lotus flower

hook

discus

arrow

sword

bow

beads

mace

bell

trident

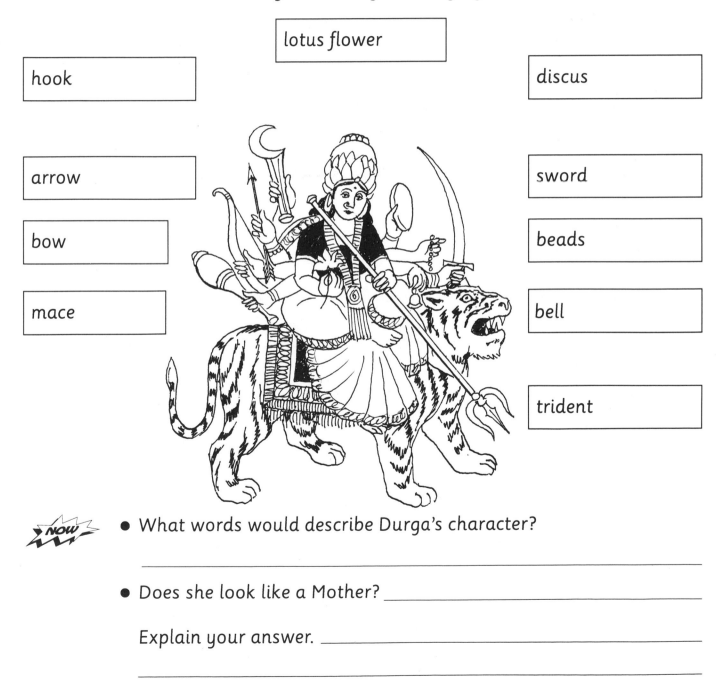

● What words would describe Durga's character?

_____

● Does she look like a Mother? _____

Explain your answer. _____

Divali – Ideas Page

Aims

- Exploring the symbolism of light and patterned doorways during **Divali**.
- Appreciation of the links between the activities of the festival and the story from the **Ramayana** (pages 26–27).

Background

Like many Hindu legends, the story of **Rama** and **Sita** represents a struggle, where good overcomes evil. Divali, which means a row of lights, celebrates this and welcomes **Lakshmi**, the goddess of good fortune and wealth who visits each home once a year.

There are regional differences in the celebration of Divali, which is celebrated in the months of Ashvin and Karttik (pages 38–39). Doorsteps are decorated with rangoli patterns and windows filled with divas (small clay lamps).

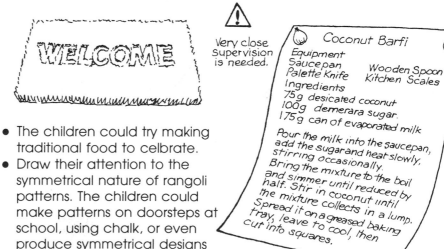

A diva lamp

Many families perform puja (pages 22–23) for Lakshmi, and businesses often close their accounts before performing puja. It is common to clean the home for Divali, put on new clothes and exchange gifts and cards.

Activities

- Before the children attempt the activity sheet, they need to know the story of Rama and Sita (pages 26–27).
- How would they welcome somebody home after a long journey or other absence? They could plan a welcome party:

Welcome Party

Who it will welcome _____
Why _____

| Decorations | Food |
| Symbols | Notices |

- Can the children describe how doorsteps sometimes welcome visitors?

WELCOME

⚠ Very close supervision is needed.

- The children could try making traditional food to celbrate.
- Draw their attention to the symmetrical nature of rangoli patterns. The children could make patterns on doorsteps at school, using chalk, or even produce symmetrical designs using computer software.

Coconut Barfi

Equipment
Saucepan
Palette Knife
Wooden Spoon
Kitchen Scales

Ingredients
75g desicated coconut
100g demerara sugar.
175g can of evaporated milk

Pour the milk into the saucepan, add the sugar and heat slowly, stirring occasionally. Bring the mixture to the boil and simmer until reduced by half. Stir in coconut until the mixture collects in a lump. Spread it on a greased baking tray, leave to cool, then cut into squares.

Developments

- Ask the children to list other festivals they know where light is a symbol. Can they explain how it is used as a symbol?

Light as a symbol of festivals		
Festival	Faith	Symbolism
Hanukkah	Judaism	Commemorating the re-dedication of the temple after the Maccabees beat the Greeks.
Christmas	Christianity	Jesus, the light of the world.

Divali

Divali celebrates the home-coming of Rama and Sita, after they had been sent away from their kingdom.

People at the time wanted to welcome them home and so decorated their houses.

At Divali many Hindus decorate their doorsteps with rangoli patterns and put lights in their windows.

'Seeing that their real lord had returned after the lapse of a long time, the subjects of northern Kosala, waving their upper garments and showering them with flowers, danced in joy.'
Bhagavad Purana 9, 10:42

- Complete and colour this rangoli pattern.
  You could try copying it using a computer.

- Doorsteps and lights in windows welcome people.
  Explain why these symbols are used at Divali.

_____

_____

Aim

- Exploring the relationship between the story of Holika and Prahlada and the festival of **Holi**.

Activities

- Some children may have difficulty reading the long name of the demon, Hiranyakashipu. Encourage them to split it into syllables. The story, like many other Hindu legends, shows good triumphing over evil. Holika loses her divine protection when she uses it for evil.
- The children could make models of the characters from this story and that of Krishna (pages 40–41) to mount on trucks or wheeled vehicles that they have made. They could build up a tableau of the celebration, including the bonfire (unlit!) and people splashed with powder paint, dancing.
- Show the children how to make halva, one of the traditional festival sweets, often eaten at Holi.

Halva

Equipment
a non-stick pan
a wooden spoon
Ingredients
100g semolina
100g ground almonds
1/2 teaspoonful ground nutmeg
300ml full cream milk
25g chopped, unsalted cashews.

heat source
baking tray

100g butter
100g sugar

Melt the butter slowly and add the semolina. Cook, stirring until it is golden. Stir in the almonds, sugar and nutmeg. Gradually add the milk, stirring until the mixture becomes thick and no longer sticks to the saucepan. Spread it in a greased baking tray and sprinkle on the cashews. Press the mixture down with a wooden spoon. When it is cool cut into squares.

Background

Holi is a spring festival celebrated in the month of Phalgun, and centres around the story of Holika and Prahlada. Holi is a noisy, joyful celebration, with a bonfire and procession. Part of the festival involves the throwing of coloured powders and the squirting of coloured water at people. Krishna is also celebrated as this sort of mischief reminds Hindus of the pranks that he played in his youth (Krishna is also an incarnation of Vishnu, who Prahlada worships in the story). In Britain the celebration usually begins at a temple with arti (worship). This is followed by a dramatisation of the stories, a procession (during which large models of the characters associated with the festival are carried on floats), dancing, singing and feasting. There is usually a bonfire, around which women may walk with small children, since fire is a symbol of purification.

An effigy of Krishna carried in procession

Developments

- Ask the children to describe differences and similarities between Holi and other Hindu festivals (see pages 38–45).

Festival	Story	Deity	Special Food	Symbols			Dancing
				Fire	Water	Light	
Janmashtami	✓	✓	✓				
Navaratri	✓	✓	✓				✓
Divali	✓	✓	✓			✓	
Holi	✓	✓	✓	✓	✓		✓

- Have they taken part in any lively, noisy festivals? How did it feel to be amongst a group of people all celebrating the same thing? They may describe festivals such as Guy Fawkes' night (because of the bonfire), New Year, Purim. Many festivals celebrate an event with a happy outcome, but the children may also be aware of festivals of a more sombre nature, such as Ash Wednesday, Lent, Yom Kippur, Easter, Ramadan.

Holi

The name of the festival called Holi comes from Holika.
   This is the story of Prahlada and Holika.

'Even as a child, he set aside his toys. His mind being completely absorbed in the Lord, he appeared as a dunce.'
Bhagavata Purana 7, 4:37

- Explain why God did not protect Holika from the fire.

_____

_____

- Who was protecting Prahlada?

_____

- Design and make models of the characters in the story. Use these to make part of a Holi procession.
- Find out about other characters that Hindus might have in a Holi procession.

Glossary

ahimsa	Non-violence. Respect for life.
arti	A welcoming ceremony when offerings are made to a deity.
atman	Soul or real self.
aum	The most sacred symbol and sound in Hinduism.
avatar	Literally 'one who descends'. A descent to Earth of a deity, sometimes thought of by non-Hindus as an incarnation.
Bhagavad Gita	Holy book, 'The Song of the Lord', spoken by Krishna.
Brahma	The deity associated with creative power.
brahmachari	A person in the first stage of life: studentship.
Brahman	The ultimate or all-pervading reality from which everything originates.
brahmin	A priest or member of the first varna.
Dassehra	Literally 'ten days'. Celebration of the victory of Rama. Often celebrated in association with the deity Durga.
Divali	Literally 'a row of lights'. Festival at the end of one year and beginning of the next.
Durga	A female deity: a form of Parvati, partner of Shiva.
Ganesha	A male deity with an elephant's head. The deity who removes obstacles.
Ganga	The holy river Ganges in India.
grihastha	A person in the second stage of life: householder.
Hanuman	The monkey warrior who helped Rama to save Sita.
Holi	The spring festival of colours, linked to the story of Holika.
Janmashtami	The birthday of Krishna.
Kali	A female deity: a form of Parvati, partner of Shiva.
Krishna	An avatar of Vishnu, whose birth is celebrated at Janmashtami.
kum kum	A red powder often used to mark the foreheads of deities and worshippers before worship.
Lakshmi	The female deity associated with good fortune.
madh	A six-sided shrine to the goddess.
Mahabharata	The Hindu epic that tells the story of the five Pandava princes.
mandir	A temple.
mantra	Literally 'that which diverts the mind'. A short prayer or chant.
moksha	The release of the soul (atman).
murti	A small statue of a deity.
Namkara	Naming ceremony.
Navaratri	The nine nights festival, in honour of Durga, just before Dassehra.
Parvati	A female deity; partner of Shiva.
pattra	A calendar that relates Hindu months, seasons and festivals to the Universal calendar.
prashad	Sanctified food.
puja	Worship.
Puranas	Hindu scriptures. Literally 'ancient'.
rakhi	A bracelet or 'tie of protection'.
Raksha Bandhan	The festival when women tie rakhis to their brothers' or male relatives' wrists.
Rama	An incarnation of the Lord. A male deity. The partner of Sita.
Ramayana	The Hindu epic that tells the story of Rama and Sita.
rangoli	Pattern traditionally seen on door steps during Divali.
Rig Veda	The first Hindu scripture.
samskar	Sacraments that begin a new stage of life.
sannyasin	A person in the final stage of life: 'renunciate', or one who has given up worldly things.
Sanskrit	The sacred language of the Hindu scriptures.
Saraswati	The female deity associated with learning.
shakti	Energy or power, especially of a female deity.
Shiva	A male deity. Literally 'kindly' or 'auspicious'. Partner of Parvati.
Sita	A female deity. Partner of Rama.
swastika	A mark of good fortune. From the Sanskrit word for well-being.
trimurti	The three deities: Brahma, Vishnu and Shiva.
Upanayana	The ceremony when the sacred thread is tied. It marks the start of learning with a guru.
vanaprasthi	A person in the third stage of life: retirement.
Varanasi	A holy place on Ganga, sacred to Shiva. Also known as Benares.
varna	A division of Hindu society. There are four varnas. A caste is a sub-division of a varna.
Vedas	Hindu holy books. Literally 'knowledge'.
Vishnu	A male deity. One of the trimurti.